The ultimate guide to eating out and dining in with French cuisine for weight loss

FRENCH 4 WEIGHT LOSS

*Australian — UK
Conversions*

WEIGHT
1 Kilogram (kg) = 2.2 Pounds (lb)

INGREDIENTS
Eggplant = Aubergine
Capsicum = Pepper
Zucchini = Courgette
Omelet = Omlette
Skimmed milk = Skim or lite milk

BODYTRIM UK
Phone 0845 873 1170
www.bodytrim.eu

Editor In Chief Alex Sisiolas
Food Director/Chef Robert Hodgson
Editing/production Michael Johnston
Photography John Fryz and
StockFood/Picture Media
Nutritionist Chris Lynton
Product Manager Sophie Leach

Design and Typesetting
Metro Graphics Group Pty Ltd
DVD Production Miller Creative Entertainment
Producer Josh Cliento
Director Michael Sutherland

French 4 Weight Loss is published by IGEA Life Sciences Pty Ltd.
GPO Box 2169, Sydney, NSW, 2001, Australia.
For general information or customer service, please phone
(within Australia) 1300 66 44 80 (International) +61 2 8023 3888
www.bodytrim.com.au

Chief Executive Officer Alex Sisiolas
Chief Operating Officer Geoff Jowett
Research & Development Manager Chris Lynton
Marketing Manager Mathew Cole

French
4 WEIGHT LOSS

bodytrim

CONTENTS

FOREWORD

For many years food has been positioned as the bad guy when it comes to losing weight. We have been told that you have to eat less and exercise more if you are to shift the kilos.

Well, after 12 extensive years of research and testing, I can say with both confidence and conviction that the bill of goods we have been sold is wrong.

The good news… food is not the enemy when it comes to losing weight, but rather it is your No.1 weapon.

My weight loss system, Bodytrim, is a globally compliant, lifestyle orientated weight management plan that uses food to melt the kilos, not strenuous exercise.

My plan caters for cuisines from all corners of the globe, and with this in mind we have created the *4 Weight Loss* by cuisine cookbook series to help you apply in practical ways the Bodytrim principles to some of your favourite foods.

To date, more than 150,000 people have transformed their bodies by eating more, not less, and without any form of strenuous exercise. This book (and the series of which it is a part) is the next step in the Bodytrim revolution.

When used as an accompaniment to Bodytrim, I believe *French 4 Weight Loss* will not only help you lose weight, but also fast-track the results by providing varied and tasty options for cooking at home.

Having road tested many of the dishes myself, I truly hope that you enjoy them as much as I did. Losing weight has never tasted so good!

Geoff Jowett (B Sp Sc)
Bodytrim Founder

INTRODUCTION

After reading and cooking from this book, you will have gained an in-depth understanding of the tips and tricks of the health and weight loss industry's 'professionals' – and be an expert in making the right, educated choices about the foods you eat when you are out and about.

The guidelines are a simple, easy-to-follow explanation of what has probably taken both Geoff and myself over 25 years collectively of research to learn. You might ask, 'How could it take *that* long?'

Well, while the health and weight loss industry over the past three decades has gone through some drastic revolutions, in some people's minds it has come full circle, back to where we started. In that time, literally hundreds of thousands of

miracle pills, celebrity-of-the-month-diets and doctor-recommended eating plans have evolved through government-sponsored dietary guidelines that in some cases only months later are turned on their head. Super-low fats, no-fats, now-you-have-to-have-good-fats, trans fats, low-GI, simple carbs, complex carbs... you get the picture.

We may have been better off to have stuck our heads in the sand for the past 20 or 30 years because today many health professionals and government bodies are finally putting up their hands to say, 'Yes, we were wrong'. But I guess hindsight is always 20/20.

So looking back is the only way to move forward. Looking back to traditional cooking methods and cuisines, real food ingredients and real food practices in the right patterns is the only way to achieve real weight loss for life.

And French is one of the age-old cuisines that fits perfectly with weight loss and weight maintenance. This is because many French dishes accompany quality, lean protein foods with fibrous vegetable and salads, which put your body in an optimum fat-burning state.

Eggs and chicken are two of the best weight loss weapons, and they feature heavily in French cooking. Eggs are the benchmark for protein foods and, let me tell you, they give you more bang for your buck than any food I know. They contain literally an alphabet of vitamins and minerals, plus they set you up for optimum weight loss.

Likewise, salad nicoise is full of flavour, colour and nutrients, protein and fibrous, starch-free carbohydrates. What better meal for weight loss? It contains omega 3, vitamins, minerals and, of course, body-cleansing chlorophyll (the green stuff in plants and food).

Rabbit and duck are widely used and are fantastic for your health and your waistline. Some group these two as 'game meat' because of the similar health benefits. Certainly, game meats are healthier, leaner, lower in saturated fat and often cheaper than other cuts (which makes it great for the waistline as well as the wallet).

Fish and seafood are also regulars at the French table. In recent years, we have learnt more about the health benefits of regularly eating fish. It promotes brain development, reduces the risk of diabetes and heart disease and is good for the skin, while also helping you lose weight.

The French are of course famous for their coffee and pastries and, as we know, drinking coffee is like adding fuel to your metabolic fire – but one thing you notice in France is that generally pastries are kept to the morning meal. Couple this with a quality protein source (or indulge on a Free Day and jump start your weight loss the following week) and the French diet fits neatly into Bodytrim eating practices.

So next time someone asks you why French people generally seem so slim, tell them that France has been following Bodytrim without even knowing it!

Chris Lynton (BSc H, GC Nutr)

CHEF ROBERT HODGSON

As far back as I can remember, I always wanted to be a chef. I think it was the first time I licked the bowl from a cake my mum had made that helped me make up my mind.

My dad hated food, so my mum would go to great lengths to get him to eat. She would cook elaborate Chinese banquets that included home-made peking duck with pancakes or Indian curries with naan bread. She opened my eyes to different ingredients and to the endless possibilities of them. I was fascinated by this and was the most eager of helpers – until it came to the cleaning up.

I grew up in the north of England and, like most chefs, kind of fell into cooking. I got a job as a kitchen hand at the local restaurant and loved the hustle and bustle of it all. It wasn't long before I was helping out on the vegetable section and studying cooking.

Cooking always seemed a logical process to me, and for the first time in my life I was top of the class. At this time, a local chef became the first chef in the UK to get three Michelin stars, and this was a great inspiration to me. I moved to the south of England to further my career, working in various restaurants and hotels, and also worked in northern France.

I moved to Australia in 1994 and soon fell in love with the land and its people. After travelling for a while and working in a creperie until I got my visa sorted, I got a job at Merrony's in Sydney's Circular Quay. This was arguably one of the best French restaurants of its time. I moved onto The Boathouse on Blackwattle Bay as sous chef under Yvan Menninere, for four years, before my first job as Head Chef, at the iconic Bayswater Brasserie in Kings Cross. I stayed there for four years before joining La Grande Bouffe.

I hope you enjoy the dishes in this book. The recipes have been adapted by me for Bodytrim from my dishes served at the restaurant. Most, especially the mains, are designed to eat with a side dish of green vegetables or garden salad.

Enjoy!

Robert Hodgson

La Grande Bouffe
758 Darling Street Rozelle
Sydney 2039 Australia
Phone +61 (02) 9818 4333
www.lagrandebouffe.com.au

LA GRANDE BOUFFE

Look at the list of awards La Grande Bouffe has won over the years and it really does live up to its reputation as 'the big feast'. Step into this charming restaurant in Sydney's Rozelle and you might have wandered into a classic French bistro on the streets of Paris.

It had been a long search to find just the right place when, in May 2004, David and Meredith Poirier decided to open their restaurant in what had been an unassuming suburban cafe on the trendy Balmain peninsula.

'We had been looking for ages all over metropolitan Sydney and this was perfect. Because the premises was previously a cafe, the bones were there,' says Meredith.

Frenchman David has spent his working life in the industry. He and Meredith met in London, where David had moved to work and improve his English. They left for Sydney three years later, in 1997, and David worked at some of the city's top-rated restaurants including Salt, Mezzaluna, MG Garage, Aria and Tabou.

La Grande Bouffe is the couple's first venture together, and even they couldn't have imagined it would become such an outstanding success, winning Best New Restaurant in the Restaurant and Catering Metropolitan awards, as well as Best Local Restaurant. 'We have been very fortunate with its popularity and success. I suppose we changed a few things as we've learnt along the way.' And it's the little things that make the whole experience. 'We had the wallpaper designed and printed especially, and we've added a few other touches.'

Perhaps beyond the fine food and superb service it is their insistence on making the locals feel welcome that has helped ensure its continued popularity. 'Most people that come in are locals, and our coffee is the best in the street for sure!' The art on the walls is from local artists also.

Of course, a restaurant is ultimately judged on its food, and David and Meredith can't praise highly enough their friend and chef Robert Hodgson. 'Rob would have to be one of our greatest additions. His food is outstanding. He is a wonderful chef and friend.'

During the day, soak up the sunlit interior with a *bol* of the aforementioned house-roasted coffee and French toast with pear, walnuts and maple syrup.

In the evenings, the dark and moody wallpaper, rich-chocolate timber floors and sultry lighting transform the interior. Savour something from the a la carte menu or sit back and be seduced by the diverse degustation.

The extensive menu is frequently updated and features classic French fare – roasted veal fillet with potato dauphinoise, trompette de la mort and foie gras. Or perhaps try the blanquette de lapin, braised rabbit with onion, herb and bread dumplings, sauteed yellow squash and green olives.

For dessert, indulge in the poached red-wine-spiced pear with vanilla mascarpone or, in true French style, opt for the assiette de fromage, a selection of fine cheeses.

This is authentic French dining at its very best – but always with a local twist.

FRENCH CUISINE

French cooking is the most famous cuisine in the world, and most Australians have tasted at least a soupçon of its delicate and piquant flavours.

Whether you have travelled to Paris and dined in the Michelin three-star establishment of the legendary Alain Ducasse, eaten souffle at your local suburban French restaurant, cooked up some French onion soup at home or just grabbed a ham and cheese croissant on the way to work, you have sampled French cuisine.

And in doing so you have touched centuries of history.

The preparation and display of food for the tables of kings, queens and the aristocracy became a high art in France and continued beyond the French Revolution as a pleasure for the tables of even the humblest peasant.

And so the tradition continues today: eating is to be enjoyed, shared with friends and family, in a celebration of the best produce, made into fine dishes all beautifully served on fine china, with exquisite glassware and linen.

And if you are preparing one of the classic French dishes – coq au vin, boeuf bourguignon, coquilles Saint Jacques, quiche Lorraine, tuna nicoise or ratatouille – there will be a story attached and an origin in one of the 26 regions that make up the country we know as France.

While some may equate French cuisine with dining in view of the Eiffel Tower, French cooking is essentially provincial. Across the hexagonal-shaped country, the soil and climate vary wildly, and so does the produce, from the truffles and foie gras of the historic south-western Perigord to the spicy peppers of the mountainous Basque country, the cabbages of Alsace Lorraine, the mustard from Dijon and the Brie, Camembert and Champagne from their namesake places on the map.

Considerable influences from the countries that border France – Spain in the south-west, Italy in the south-east and Belgium and German on its northern boundaries – have shaped French cooking. Nevertheless, the ritual of dining as an event originated in Paris, which considers itself the national, and indeed the international, capital of fine cuisine. It is one of the highlights of French culture and society.

From the early days, however, those who could cook were willing to share the secrets of their table with the masses and their innovations are still in use today. The first ever French cookbook, written in 1652 by the chef Francois Pierre La Varenne, included directions for making a roux, the mixture of flour and butter used to thicken soups (before roux, cooks had simply used bread for thickening).

Another chef-author produced a book in 1691, for the first time in print mentioning a marinade. Marie-Antoine Carême was born in 1784, five years before the French Revolution's onset, and grew up to be a most innovative chef. In his writings, souffles appeared for the first time along with more than 100 sauces. It was inventions such as these that vaulted French cuisine into becoming the leader, firstly of European and then global haute cuisine.

In the modern era, French cuisine was to depart from its regional character, under the influence of the 20th century chef Georges Escoffier, and a national cuisine of heavily creamed meats and desserts came to typify the cooking of France.

Nouvelle cuisine, a lighter version with smaller portions, swept into fashion before France once again embraced its diversity, and the new cooking emphasised the bountiful fresh produce of France, where merely eating a vine-grown tomato from the market can be a heady experience.

Soon more and more tourists began to travel to the regions for a particular type of cheese and wine, or to sample the peasant cuisine and bourgeois dishes unadorned by heavy sauces created from difficult, finicky recipes.

As a result, in the past 20 years the simple baguette with ham and cheese or pate have become commonplace in cafes outside France, and simplified recipes have brought dishes like cassoulet, creme brulee and even truffle omelets into the realm of the home cook.

So, as the French became masters of combining beautifully prepared food with their regional wines, they also gave to the rest of the world the convivial art of fine dining in good company.

If you have never indulged in French cooking before, start a revolution in your kitchen today. By doing it the Bodytrim way you wil stay lean for life.

MUST-HAVE
INGREDIENTS

Basic techniques of French cuisine carry over to every other style of cooking, but always with an emphasis on the best, freshest ingredients available.

Dairy

Butter (unsalted), milk (full cream is best for cooking but you can substitute skim or Lite), sour cream, cheese (gruyere, for example).

Garlic

Synonymous with French and Mediterranean-style cooking, garlic has many health promotional properties. Garlic cloves are cooked whole, chopped, crushed or minced.

Mustard

Most famous is the classic one from Dijon. Other varieties work just as well with vinaigrettes, sauces, steaks, pork, seafood and vegetables.

Olive oil

Perfect for salads or drizzled over vegetables and fish, this is one of the healthiest oils.

Nutmeg

Has a distinctive aroma and delicate flavour. Can be grated raw or store bought.

Parsley

The French sprinkle freshly chopped parsley liberally over meat and vegetable dishes, often mixing it with garlic to serve with fried or sauteed dishes. The flat-leafed variety has the most flavour.

Red-wine vinegar

The word 'vinegar' derives from the French 'vin aigre', meaning 'sour wine' and is a staple in most French homes. White-wine vinegar is used to make Hollandaise and Bearnaise sauces, vinaigrettes, soups and stews.

Stock (beef and chicken)

Used in soups, sauces and cassoulets. Traditionalists would have you make your own, but good stocks are available in stores.

Sea salt (fleur de sel)

A salt with delicate flavour. It has a higher mineral content and it is less processed than table salt.

HERBS

Don't be afraid to experiment with herbs, and not just those listed here.

Basil

Used in salads and dressings, cooked with meat or vegetables. Fresh from the garden is best but you can buy it in jars.

Chervil

This is a favourite for the French but must be used fresh. It has a subtle flavour and is delicious in omelets. Add just before serving if used in a sauce.

Parsley

Chop fresh into salad dressings, cook in sauces or use as a garnish.

Herbes de Provence

A staple of French country cooking, usually sold in a bag made up of thyme, marjoram, rosemary, basil, bay leaf, and lavender.

Sage

A pungent herb most commonly used to flavour white meats and pasta.

Sorrel

Perfect with fish, it has a slight bitterness.

Tarragon

Used in chicken, fish and egg dishes, the French variety has the most flavour.

USEFUL UTENSILS

KNIVES

Chef's knife

For dicing, carving and slicing. Should be solid and heavy and always very sharp.

All-purpose knife

Smaller than a chef's knife, but just as sharp. Use to peel, mince, slice or cut small ingredients.

Filleting knife

Has a long, soft blade and is good for filleting fish and trimming skin and sinew from meat.

Paring knife

Good for peeling vegetables like onions, and for boning small birds.

Serrated knife

For cutting bread, terrines, tarts, etc.

Sharpening steel

Essential for always keeping your knives sharp.

SPOONS

Metal spoon (or ladle)

For saucing dishes, serving soups and removing food from pots.

Slotted spoon

For lifting food such as poached eggs from cooking liquid.

Wooden spoon

Good for cooking custards and scrambled eggs, for instance. You should have one for cooking pastries and desserts and one for meat dishes.

OTHER USEFUL ITEMS

Bowls

It is always good to have several different sized bowls, depending on the amounts you are preparing.

Colander

For draining food after washing or cooking in liquid such as when poaching.

Conical sieve

Good for stocks, purees, sauces and soups, etc, that need lumps or impurities removed.

Fish slice

Great for turning items in frying pans, not just fish.

Food processor or liquidiser

For pastry, soups and purees, for instance.

Garlic crusher

Good for squeezing garlic flesh direct into dishes, when finely sliced isn't enough. Often recipes also refer to "pressing" the garlic into the dish.

Grater

If your electric mixer cannot grate or slice.

Mandolin

Like an upside-down plane used for cutting vegetables into a uniform size and thickness. Ideal when vegetables need to be cut into slivers or matchsticks (julienned).

Salad spinner

For properly drying salads and herbs after washing.

Whisk

An absolute must for beating and mixing ingredients. Ideal for smoothing any lumps from wet mixtures, and the surest way to a silky sauce or mayonnaise.

CLASSIC
COOKING STYLES

Baking or roasting

The traditional way of slowly cooking food in the oven using dry heat.

Blanching

Involves boiling food in water very briefly before plunging into cold water, ready to be cooked using other methods. Some fruits are first blanched to loosen their skin and make peeling easier. Herbs may be blanched first to minimise their smell and strong flavour.

Braising

Typically, when meat is slow-cooked in liquid (stock) in the oven or on the stove-top over a very low heat. It is often referred to as pot roasting.

Flambe

The word flambe means "flame" in French. This is a style of cooking designed to add flavour, but is also used for dramatic effect at the end of cooking, when alcohol is added to a hot pan to create a burst of flames.

Broiling or grilling

These two styles both involve cooking an oiled piece of food under direct, high heat.

Poaching

This is gently simmering so-called fragile food in salted water (eggs), milk, stock (poultry) or wine (fish).

Saute

Uses a small amount of fat in a shallow pan to cook food quickly over high heat. The aim is to brown the food while preserving its colour, moisture and flavour. Common with more tender cuts such as filet mignon that are traditionally served very pink. Similar to pan-frying except the food is moved about continually to ensure even heat distribution.

Stir-fry

A very healthy Chinese style adopted by western chefs, this method uses very little oil. Meat and vegetables are cut into small pieces or slivers and pan-fried in hot fat, sesame oil or sunflower oil, shaking and stirring constantly so the food is cooked through but still retains some firmness.

Sweating

An important technique usually applied to chopped vegetables such as onions and shallots at the beginning of cooking using a frypan. Use only a little oil in the base of the pan, and the heat should be as gentle as possible so the food doesn't colour but still softens.

Searing and pan-frying

Large pieces of meat are pan-fried and just-browned all over, usually before being finished off in the oven. Use a medium-to-high heat - too low and the juices will escape and you'll be left with a beige mess.

"

The variety in
my diet has
increased,
my food is
now fresh and
unprocessed.

Caroline Girke

"

Adapting French Cuisine

4 WEIGHT LOSS AND MAINTENANCE

INCLUDING TIPS AND TRICKS FOR EATING OUT

HEALTHY CHOICES

No matter the cuisine, there will always be healthy and not-so-healthy options to choose from, and French is no different.

While the French are noted for their love of rich food and wine, the foundation of their cuisine remains the importance of taking the time to savour a meal with family and friends – and always in moderation.

The French are not a 'supersize me' culture and they have long understood the power of smaller, more frequent meals to help increase the body's fat-burning ability.

Of course, whether out at your local cafe or a five-star restaurant or at home cooking for family, there are some general dos and don'ts when it comes to French food.

It won't come as any great surprise that French breads, cheeses and pastries are some of the biggest barriers to weight loss. So avoid the quiches, Camembert, croissants, muffins and éclairs you find among the many other famous fattening French fancies.

Likewise, leave the souffles, creme caramels and crème brulees for your free days, as these high-sugar foods will only put you on the carb craving train and never let you off. Staying clear of these foods will have you on track to your weight loss goal in no time.

Instead, go for any of the many different and delicious egg-based dishes such as omelets or lean protein foods such as sea bream with mixed salad or rabbit with ratatouille.

One great thing about most French restaurants is that the portions are generally a sensible size, so half your weight loss battle is won when eating out. Just make sure you stick to the many lean protein dishes such as veal, lamb, beef, seafood or chicken. And, no matter what, always stay clear of carb, calorie and fat rich baked-potato dishes (unless it's a free day).

If all else fails, you can always order the quiche and don't eat the pastry! In fact, quiche Lorraine without the pastry is a perfect choice for anyone watching their weight, and you can adapt it yourself at home. Simply line a small muffin tray with baking paper instead of pastry, pour the egg filling into the individual moulds and you have created for yourself a perfect and tasty fat-burning meal or snack.

The good news about cooking at home is that you can always adjust or adapt recipes and cuisines to suit yourself and your weight loss goals.

It's easy, once you know what to look for. The rule of thumb is to always choose a lean protein portion accompanied by an unlimited serving of fibrous vegetables or salad.

> " Eating out and losing weight is so easy when you know how.
>
> *Brian Stewart*
> "

THE POWER OF FOOD

Sure, Bodytrim is helping people to lose 20, 30, 40 even 50+ kilos, but it does not stop there.

Letters of excitement and thanks pour in to the Bodytrim offices daily from around the world. People who had suffered weight-related health diseases for many years have reversed type-2 diabetes or decreased their cholesterol and blood pressure and risk of heart disease. Some have been told by their doctors they no longer need to take any medication … ever again!

This truly shows the power of food in ensuring good health and weight loss, something we perhaps always knew, but which has become lost in the bustle of modern living. However, it is a simple and, for some, inconvenient truth that we humans are natural-born hunter-gathers – who no longer hunt or gather!

This is the reason for the many diseases that plague the world. Think about it, some of today's most prevalent diseases were once unheard of. These diseases have become so common in the past 20 or 30 years that government and health agencies even created a new classification for them: lifestyle diseases. They are indeed diseases of our lifestyle, of a way of living that flies in the face of the body's natural metabolism and design. And the biggest culprit has been the highly refined, high-carb, low-fat diet pushed by top healthcare professionals.

Of course, beyond the power it gives the body to combat disease, eating the way nature intended also immediately unlocks the body's fat-burning potential. That's right, it's not too late. Did you know that every cell in your body will regenerate over the next 12 months? So when you eat the right foods at the right intervals, you can transform your body and your health.

BACK TO THE FUTURE

We have to look at where we came from if we are to successfully make inroads against these diseases of civilisation and wage war on obesity.

Bodytrim has done just that, adapting the hunter-gatherer diet to suit today's modern, fast-paced lifestyle. It not only teaches you how to feed your body as it was meant to be, with powerful results, but also acknowledges the popularity and availability of processed foods with starch-based carbohydrates by showing you how to adapt them into your everyday diet and lifestyle.

THE THREE Ws

As a society, we need to learn about the three Ws of weight loss

What to eat

When to eat it

And, most importantly, **Why**

Armed with this knowledge, you will not only achieve fast and permanent weight loss, but also become immune to the sinister plots of the marketing men and their latest miracle method of the month. You will have won your personal war against diet companies who attempt to sabotage us with gimmicks and quackery.

Bodytrim is a fully packaged system giving you the weapons you need in that battle. Even better, once you have mastered the secrets you can apply them to any cuisine style and enjoy the full benefits of food without thinking of it as your enemy.

People who follow the Bodytrim principles quickly discover that food is in fact their No.1 weapon and friend when it comes to sculpting a trim, beautiful body that people will notice.

HOW TO USE THIS BOOK

The Bodytrim *4 Weight Loss* series is designed to go hand in hand with the Bodytrim lifestyle. Bodytrim is all about learning how to use food as the key to achieve your dream body.

The recipes in *French 4 Weight Loss* are designed to set your body up in the optimal environment to burn fat fast and easy. With this cookbook, you will learn how to make the best food decisions when eating out, as well as how to cook quick, delicious, full-flavoured meals that the whole family can enjoy at home. You will learn that losing weight is not about starving then fighting your cravings.

With Bodytrim and the *4 Weight Loss* series you will learn how to fall in love with food again and never have to be embarrassed about what you're eating. And you will be able to eat rich restaurant-quality meals at home every day. All the recipes in *French 4 Weight Loss* can be adjusted to fit each phase of the Bodytrim system, whether you are in the weight loss phase or already at your goal and in the weight maintenance phase. Throughout, you'll find tips for adjusting most of the recipes to suit your needs for breakfast, lunch or dinner. Just remember to always match the protein serving sizes to your individual serving size suggestion.

Because Bodytrim is not a diet but a lifestyle, it is important that you continue to enjoy food while keeping within the Bodytrim guidelines as much as possible to ensure optimum results. All meals are nutritionally balanced to fit within the Bodytrim system and, as mentioned, if in a weight maintenance phase you have the option of including a carb portion with your lunch main meal.

This carb portion can be anything, and in *French 4 Weight Loss* you'll find handy suggested options.

As with free days, we always recommended nutritionally balanced meals for best results, but treating yourself, in moderation, is definitely a part of the Bodytrim way.

3+3 = FAT FREE

With Bodytrim you will never again have hunger pangs because it is all about eating more to lose more. We incorporate a 3+3 = Fat Free concept that will have your metabolism firing and the fat melting off you in no time. That is, three main meals and three snacks. It is a key component you will learn about with Bodytrim that, when used in the right way, will unlock your fat burning potential. Hence, the recipes in *French 4 Weight Loss* are designed to give you options for your three main meals.

Bodytrim is broken up into three easy-to-follow phases: carb detox, weight loss and weight maintenance.

The **carb detox phase** (phase 1) is an important start to your weight loss goal. This phase will deplete your body's carbohydrate stores, give you fast results, eliminate those sugar cravings that bring us all undone, elevate and regulate your mood, help you bounce out of bed in the morning and let you say goodbye to those 3pm energy slumps, as well as keep you feeling full and satisfied all the time.

After completing this important phase you then go into the **weight loss phase** (phase 2). This phase will educate you on all the right foods to get you to your weight loss goal in no time. It is so easy, simple and straight forward – and let's not forget the weekly free day! The free day is an integral part of the sustainability of the Bodytrim system. Not only does it allow you the freedom to eat out and let your hair down, but it also helps to increase your metabolism and make you burn more fat in the following week. No more dreaded plateaus, no more abstaining from foods only to be overcome with cravings.

Once you have reached your goal weight, you slip into the **weight maintenance phase** (phase 3), which will keep you at your goal weight for life! No more losing weight only to go and put it all back on, and then some.

WHY BODYTRIM

If you are not already following the Bodytrim system, drop into your local book or health food store and get your hands on a kit today.

Alternatively, visit www.bodytrim.com.au or call 1300 66 44 80 to order. You won't be disappointed.

While the recipes in this book are all Bodytrim compliant and approved, they are only examples of meals that measure up to the Bodytrim standard. Permanent weight management comes down to two things: education and ongoing motivation.

As such, the Bodytrim system is designed to equip you with all that master trainer and weight loss guru Geoff Jowett has learnt over the past decade about physique transformation through eating the right foods in the right frequency.

Simply following the recipes in this book will not ensure permanent weight loss. People need to know not just **What** to eat, but also **Why** they are eating it. When a person is equipped with the knowledge in the Bodytrim system, and is a part of the Bodytrim community, known as 'Trim Club', then the chances of permanent success increase exponentially.

Look to these *4 Weight Loss* cookbooks for examples and cooking suggestions relative to your favourite cuisines, however, always remember that they are intended as an accompaniment to Bodytrim.

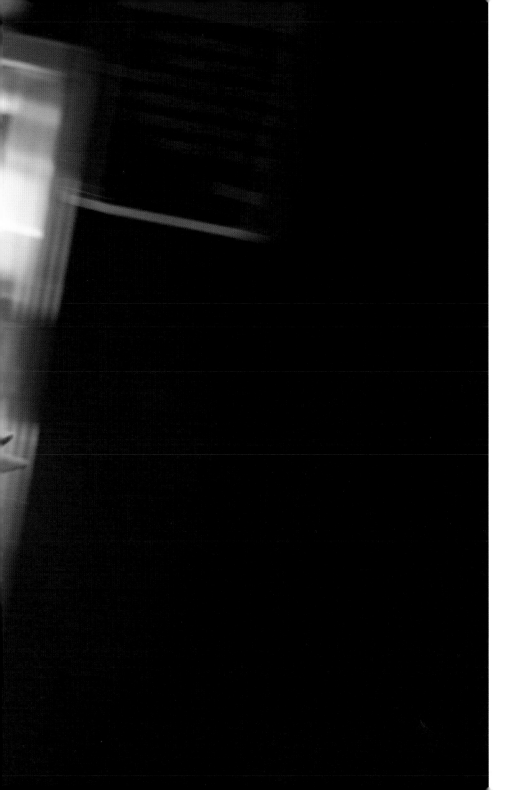

"
Be confident
to ask the chef
about what's
in the dish,
and modify it
if needed.

Peta Adams

"

EATING OUT
TIPS AND TRICKS

With Bodytrim you will more than likely have at least one portion of either chicken, beef, pork, lamb or other animal protein food in your week (unless vegetarian).

Always look for a lean, quality cut of meat when available. If the meat has skin on, make sure to remove this beforehand and always trim visible fats from your meal before eating. Remember that these saturated fats are just empty energy, and eating too many of them has been found to contribute to many lifestyle problems.

This is also true with foods that are deep-fried. Although the food in the first place may have been a healthy option, it becomes unhealthy or weight loss inhibiting once deep-fried.

Don't pay attention to the marketing ploy of 'deep-fried in cholesterol free oil'. Nearly all vegetable oils are cholesterol-free to begin with, but when used for deep-frying the 'good' fats become altered and can transform into the very unhealthy 'trans' fats.

This is not good for health and not good for your weight loss success.

Also remember: If your portion is too large use the cues listed on page 49) and only eat what you need. You can ask for a 'doggy bag' to take home for your next snack, or share a main meal with a friend. This makes eating out so easy.

Alternatively, if you don't feel comfortable asking to take some home with you, have the correct serving portion and leave what you don't want. Then signal for your plate to be removed so you won't pick. Out of sight is out of mind. This is very effective.

Avoid ordering foods that have the words 'double', 'jumbo', 'super', 'deluxe' or 'mega' as these generally suggest that the portions are going to be oversized.

When ordering, it's OK to ask for your meal to be grilled, steamed, shared between two, with dressing on the side, sauce on the side, pre divided or prepared with less fat.

You can have it your way!

It's OK to ask for your meal to be grilled, steamed or with dressing or sauce on the side.

CARE FOR A BEVERAGE?

Alcohol is fine in moderation and can sometimes be a staple for celebratory meals or just nice to have when eating out. It is fine if you choose to exclude alcohol while on Bodytrim, and you can still dine with people who drink alcohol without looking like an outcast.

So why not stay refreshed and on top of your goals by choosing a different drink option:

A glass of sparkling water with sliced lemon

A virgin mary – tomato juice with a dash of hot pepper/Tabasco

An iced diet/sugar-free softdrink with or without lemon slice

SOCIAL SITUATIONS

Getting a little friendly pressure to have 'just a bite' of a food that is not recommended? We have all been there. Don't worry, people are not trying to purposely sabotage your weight loss results, they are just offering as a gesture of courtesy. But you can still enjoy dining out and other social events while losing weight.

It's OK to say 'no' to an offer of food. In fact, when you practice saying 'no' to others you begin to say 'yes' to yourself. You say 'yes' to the choices that serve your interests and take you closer to your goals. Keep your explanation short. There is no reason to share your personal goals unless you want to.

Make your mantra: 'Thanks [reason] thanks' to refuse an offer of food. For example: 'Thanks for asking, but I'm full' or 'Thank-you, anyways'. Or keep it short: 'No, I'm fine thank-you'.

Do not feel you have to give in or conform to what everyone is doing. You will actually be shown more respect by people in your social setting if you do what you – not others – feel like.

EATING OUT ON YOUR FREE DAY

This integral part of the Bodytrim program not only helps keep your metabolism blazing, but it will give you a 'get out of jail free' pass one day a week. So if you feel like eating out or just relaxing over a drink and favourite food then this is the perfect day.

Bodytrim's flexibility allows you to do this one day a week for the suggested two main meals and to have whatever you feel like.

Obviously, you can still use the Bodytrim recommendations and include some other foods that you generally do not eat.

Remember, the free day can fall on any day of the week you choose and it does not need to be exactly seven days from the last. Just try to keep it to one per calendar week.

How could losing weight, enjoying eating and feeling and looking great be any easier?

6 EASY STEPS TO REMEMBER WHEN DINING OUT

STEP 1

Have a snack before you head out

Have a small snack or a serving of a sugar-free fibre supplement about 30 minutes before heading out to a restaurant. Eating out is supposed to be enjoyable and relaxing. People usually like to sit and chat, and most restaurants will serve your meal around 20-30 minutes after being seated. Add on travel time and this is at least 50-60 minutes before you get your meal.

Heading out to eat when you're already hungry can be counterproductive to weight loss. You may find that you go over the recommended 2-3 hours time frame and/or end up being so ravenous (as a result of low blood sugar levels) that you start to crave high-carb foods and start 'picking' at the entrees such as breads or end up ordering carb-rich foods. And you will tend to dramatically over-eat when your meal arrives.

STEP 2

**Your worst enemy:
The bread basket**

Bread is loaded with simple carbs (mainly white bread, the worst option), which are no good for weight loss. It usually won't do much to satisfy your hunger, but instead will load your bloodstream with sugars, set you up for an insulin spike and give you cravings for the rest of the day.

Your best option is to skip the usual bread order (if your fellow diners don't mind) or order a minimum serving of breads and let others take what they need, hopefully leaving none.

Always try to position the bread basket out of your reach.

STEP 3

**Stay away from pasta,
rice and potatoes**

If the meal that you would like has rice, potatoes or pasta listed on the menu then ask if it can be swapped for a serving of vegetables or salad. Most places will gladly do this, so don't be afraid to ask.

Think of it this way: 'I am actually doing them a favour because veg and salad is cheaper for them to give me, so why wouldn't they gladly do this?'.

You can always order a side of vegetables – roasted, broiled, braised, baked, steamed or even sauteed is fine.

If there is a cheesy sauce, ask for it on the side. Then you can use it to dip your veg in, and you'll be satisfied with using only half of what you would if it was poured on top.

STEP 4

Water is your weight loss friend

Water has multiple health benefits and many of us do not drink enough. When dehydrated, the body cannot perform at its peak and its weight loss processes will be hindered.

Always ask for water when eating out. Most places will supply a bottle of tap or you can buy spring or sparkling.

Try having a glass of water while you wait for your meal and another with your meal. This will slow your eating, aid digestion and put you on the right track to weight loss.

If you decide to have an alcoholic drink, this is fine in moderation and should not hinder your results. Red wine is probably the best option for weight loss (and may even help lower insulin response, as it is high in a mineral called chromium). Spirits with sugar-free mixers and low-carb beers are allowable, but remember to keep your water intake up because alcohol can dehydrate the body.

STEP 5

Control your portions

Eating the right portions is a must for any weight loss goal. This is not to say that you must carry your kitchen scales around everywhere with you to stick to your protein or carb portion sizes.

Bodytrim is a weight loss program that fits with your lifestyle. As such, it is not realistic for anyone to stick to all the specific guidelines all the time.

STEP 6

Don't sweat the small stuff

You will have a much better time eating out if you're not worrying about having 102g of protein food instead of the recommended 100g.

The Bodytrim system is flexible and if you try to stick with it 95% of the time you will still see great results. Keep the recommendations in mind and use familiar cues to approximate the portions that are needed for serving and portion size.

A few easy cues are

Tip of thumb = 1 teaspoon

Whole thumb = 1 tablespoon

½ orange or small fist = ½ cup

Baseball or light bulb = 1 cup

Size of your palm = 100g (4oz) protein food (depending on male or female)

Deck of cards = 90g (3oz) protein food

"
Eating out
is great fun.
Don't worry
about the
small things,
like too much
sauce. Just
avoid the
bread
basket!

Sharon Houwen

"

Recipes

4 WEIGHT LOSS
AND MAINTENANCE

Chef's tip

I have been asked for this recipe more than any other I use at the restaurant. This recipe makes about 500ml (18fl oz) of dressing, which sounds like a lot, but it lasts forever in an old wine bottle in the fridge. It is also quite strong flavoured so you don't need to use a lot.

For many of the recipes in this book, green salad is a perfect accompaniment.

FRENCH DRESSING

100ml (4fl oz) white wine vinegar

1 dessertspoon Dijon mustard

3 peeled shallots

300ml (10fl oz) vegetable oil

Salt & pepper

Method

Place vinegar, mustard and shallots in a liquidiser or food processor and blend. With the motor still running, slowly drizzle in the oil. Season with salt and pepper to taste.

Makes about 500ml (18fl oz)

" I have re-learnt my true portion size and never feel hungry.

Leah Chalwell

"

Fresh herb omelet with persian feta
Page 65

EGGS

Chef's tip

How to poach eggs

The eggs must be fresh. Heat a litre of water until simmering, but not boiling, and add 4 tspn white vinegar. Crack your egg into a cup to make sure the yolk has not broken. Gently drop the eggs into simmering water for 3-8 minutes, depending on how hard you like them. Remove with a slotted spoon to drain off the water, patting the spoon on a clean towel.

For breakfast, serve with a slice of multigrain toast.

POACHED EGGS WITH ASPARAGUS AND SPINACH

2 bundles of asparagus

4 eggs

4 tspn white vinegar

2 tspn olive oil

300g (10oz) baby spinach

Method

Blanch the asparagus in plenty of boiling, salted water for 4-5 minutes and put aside. Poach eggs (see chef's tip opposite page). While the eggs are poaching, heat olive oil in a large frying pan and saute the spinach until just wilted. Serve the spinach onto the middle of the plates, lay the asparagus on top, then a poached egg.

Serves 2-4

For breakfast, serve with a slice of sourdough bread.

WITLOF SALAD WITH HAM HOCK
AND POACHED EGG

200g (7oz) shredded ham hock meat

2 large heads witlof

100ml (4fl oz) French dressing
(see page 55)

Salt & pepper

4 poached eggs
(see poaching tips on page 58)

Method

Allow 2 hours for the ham hock.

Boil 2 ham hocks in plenty of water for about 2 hours
(if you can do this a day in advance even better). Allow to cool then
remove the meat from the bone (this should be very easy!). Discard
the skin and any excess fat (keep the liquid as this is delicious for
soup – see ham hock, vegetable and chervil soup on page 111).

Slice witlof into rounds and add the shredded ham hock and French
dressing, season with salt and pepper, divide between 4 serving
bowls and pop a poached egg on top of each.

Serves 3-4

If you have extra ham hock left, it is great with lentils, is low in fat
and tastes so much better than the processed stuff.

For breakfast serve with a slice of multi grained toast or fresh fruit.

OEUFS SUR LE PLAT
(EGGS WITH MUSHROOM AND SPINACH)

4 large field mushrooms,
peeled and sliced

100g (4oz) spinach, steamed and chopped
(frozen spinach is OK, but fresh is better)

Salt & pepper

4-8 free range eggs

Truffle oil (optional)

4 oeufs sur le plat dishes
(or ramekins)

Method

Season mushrooms with salt and pepper and bake in hot
oven for 3-8 minutes, until soft (this intensifies the flavour).
Spread cooked mushrooms on the bottom of 4 oeufs sur le plat
dishes. Pile spinach evenly on top of the mushrooms and season.
Crack the eggs on top. Cook in a medium oven for 8-10 minutes.
Serve with wholegrain toast. Drizzle with a little truffle oil before
serving, if you like.

Serves 4

Oeufs sur le plat simply means "eggs on a plate". There are
special dishes in France for cooking this recipe, but a ramekin
works just as well. The mushrooms can be cooked in advance
and will keep in the fridge for about 3 days.

For breakfast or a weight maintenance lunch, serve with a slice of multigrain toast.

FRESH HERB OMELET WITH PERSIAN FETA

1-2 free range eggs

Salt & pepper

10 fresh tarragon leaves,
picked and chopped

5 sprigs fresh chervil,
picked and chopped

1 tspn chopped fresh parsley

Olive oil

15g (½oz) persian feta

Method

Crack eggs into a bowl. Whisk in salt, pepper and the herbs. Heat a small nonstick pan on medium heat. Add a touch of olive oil and pour in the egg mixture. Wait for about 10 seconds, until the mixture begins to set around the outside. Pull the set part inwards to allow the liquid to go towards the outside. Continue this process until the mix has nearly set in the middle. Add the feta, roll into a sausage shape and eat immediately.

Serves 1-2

Before non-stick pans were invented omelets were considered one of the most difficult things to prepare because you had to get the pan hot enough for the egg not to stick, but not too hot otherwise it burns.

"

I am always
happy to tell
people why
my smile is a
little wider
whilst my hips
are getting
slimmer.

Sue Johnson

"

Pageot sur ratatouille
(sea bream on ratatouille)
Page 81

SEAFOOD

For a weight maintenance lunch, have with a small serve of fresh fruit.

SALAD NICOISE

250g (8oz) green beans

2 sprigs summer savory

1 red onion

200g (7oz) tomatoes

1 green capsicum

½ cucumber

4 tbsp black olives

12 anchovy fillets

1 small romaine lettuce

200g (7oz) tuna

6 tbsp olive oil

2 hard-boiled eggs

2 tbsp lemon juice

2 cloves garlic, peeled and crushed

Salt & freshly ground pepper

A few basil leaves

Method

Wash, top and tail the beans and cook in boiling, salted water with the summer savory for 6-8 minutes, until cooked but still retaining a little bite. Take out, refresh in cold water, drain and set aside.

Peel and quarter the onion and cut into thin strips. Wash the tomatoes, cut into wedges and remove the cores. Wash and trim the capsicum and cut into thin strips. Peel the cucumber, halve lengthwise, scrape out the seeds with a spoon and slice thinly. Drain the olives and anchovies. Season with salt and pepper. Wash the lettuce, spin dry and tear into bite-sized pieces. Carefully mix the lot together.

Wash the tuna, pat dry, cut into strips and fry briefly in 2 tbsp olive oil.

To serve, cut the eggs into wedges and scatter over the salad with the tuna. Mix the remaining olive oil with the lemon juice and the garlic, season with salt and pepper and drizzle over the salad. Garnish with basil leaves.

Serves 3-5

POACHED SALMON WITH SALSA VERDI

Salmon

4 x 150g (5oz)
salmon portions

Poaching stock

1 carrot, chopped

1 celery stick, chopped

½ onion, chopped

½ leek, chopped

Zest of ½ lemon

2 sprigs thyme

1 sprig parsley

2 bay leaves

A clove of garlic

1 tspn salt

1 tspn peppercorns

1.5 litres (2.5 pints) water

150ml (5fl oz) white wine

Salsa verdi

½ bunch tarragon

½ bunch parsley

½ bunch basil

½ bunch mint

1 tbsp capers

1 tbsp Dijon mustard

20ml (0.7fl oz) red wine vinegar

50ml (1.6fl oz) olive oil

Method

Mix all of the poaching stock ingredients together in a large pan, bring to the boil and simmer for about 2 minutes. Place the salmon into the simmering stock and cook for 4 minutes, then turn off the heat and leave to sit for a further 2 minutes.

Put all of the salsa verdi ingredients into a blender and pulse until an even paste forms (you can do this in advance). Take out the salmon, plate up and drizzle with the salsa verdi.

Serves 4-6

GAZPACHO WITH KING PRAWNS

1 red capsicum, roughly chopped

1 red onion, roughly chopped

2 cloves garlic

8 roma tomatoes, roughly chopped

3 tbsp sherry vinegar

⅓ cup olive oil

A dash of Tabasco sauce

A dash of Worcestershire sauce

Salt & pepper

12 large king prawns, cooked

Baby herbs, for garnish

Method

Place all of the ingredients except the prawns (and baby herbs) into a liquidiser or food processor and blend thoroughly until quite smooth. Pass through a fine sieve to remove any fibrous bits. Peel, head and de-vein prawns, slice lengthways and divide between 4 chilled soup bowls. Pour the soup around the outside. Garnish with baby herbs, if you like.

Serves 2-4

Three sardines is probably over the allowed protein, but you don't eat the head, tail or backbone, so it evens out in the end.

GRILLED SARDINES WITH CAPSICUM AND PRESERVED LEMON SALAD

12 whole, cleaned sardines
(fresh if you can)

2 tbsp olive oil

Salt & pepper

1 pinch ground cumin

Salad

1 red capsicum

1 green capsicum

3 ripe tomatoes, seeded
and cut into 1cm dice

4 spring onions, chopped

2 tspn white wine vinegar

1 small garlic clove, crushed

1 tbsp preserved lemon,
finely chopped

Method

For the salad: Cut the capsicums into 4 lengthways, remove the stalk and seeds and put under the grill skin-side up for about 10 minutes, until the skin is blistering and blackening. Remove from the tray, put into a bowl, cover with clingfilm and leave for about 10 minutes. Remove the skin and cut into rough 1cm dice. Put into a bowl with the tomatoes, spring onions, olive oil, vinegar, garlic and preserved lemon. Season with salt and black pepper and mix well. Add a little of the juice from the preserved lemon, to taste.

Pre-heat grill or BBQ to hottest temperature. Brush sardines with olive oil and sprinkle with salt, black pepper and cumin. Grill for about 3 minutes on each side, until the skin is crisp. Place on a plate, spoon the salad over and serve.

Serves 3-4

Mahi mahi is one of the cheaper fish when in season.

ROAST MAHI MAHI WITH EGGPLANT PUREE AND SAUCE VIERGE

4 x 150g (5oz) pieces mahi mahi

Eggplant puree

1 medium eggplant

⅓ cup olive oil

Juice of 1 lemon

Salt & pepper

Sauce vierge

2 tomatoes, seeded and diced

1 tspn chopped chives

1 tspn chopped basil

1 tspn chervil

¼ tspn ground coriander seed

1tbsp white wine vinegar

3tbsp olive oil

Method

For the eggplant puree: Cut the eggplant in half and score the flesh inside. Place on a roasting tray, drizzle over the olive oil, cover with foil and cook in a medium oven for 40 minutes. Allow to cool. Scoop out the eggplant pulp and puree in a food processor, adding the lemon juice, some of the olive oil from the eggplant tray and salt and pepper to taste.

Roast the mahi mahi in a hot oven until done how you like it (try to get a bit of colour in the fish without overcooking it). Just before serving, quickly mix together all of the sauce vierge ingredients. Spoon some eggplant puree onto the serving plates, place the mahi mahi on top and spoon the sauce vierge over.

Serves 4-6

There are many different versions of sauce vierge.
It means "virgin sauce" in French, as it is not cooked.

> ❝
> I would
> recommend
> Bodytrim to
> anyone who
> doesn't mind
> doing their
> workout in
> the kitchen
> instead of
> the gym!
>
> *Makaela Owen*
> ❞

For a weight
maintenance lunch,
serve with a piece
of toast.

KING PRAWNS WITH SMOKED AUBERGINE PUREE, RADICCHIO AND WITLOF

2 tbsp olive oil

Salt & pepper

8 green king prawns,
peeled and de-veined

1 tbsp white wine

1 head radicchio, roughly chopped

1 head witlof, roughly chopped

¼ bunch dill, picked

Aubergine puree

1 large eggplant

2 cloves garlic, chopped

Juice of 1 lemon

Salt & pepper

Method

For the puree: Put the eggplant on an open flame on the gas burner and turn with a pair of tongs until it is blackened all over, about 6 minutes. Place in a bowl and allow to cool. Remove the blackened skin and place the flesh in a food processor, add garlic and lemon juice and season to taste. Set aside

Heat the olive oil, season the prawns and fry in a hot pan until they start to turn pink, about 2 minutes. Add the white wine, add the radicchio and witlof leaves and remove pan from the heat immediately. Spoon aubergine puree onto the plates and place the prawns on top. Garnish with pickled dill.

Serves 3-4

This aubergine puree recipe is basically a take on baba ghannouj. It is delicious by itself or as a dip.

PAGEOT SUR RATATOUILLE
(SEA BREAM ON RATATOUILLE)

Ratatouille

2 onions

4 cloves garlic

4 tomatoes

2 zucchini

1 large aubergine (eggplant)

2 red capsicum

4 sprigs thyme

4 tspn olive oil

Sea salt & pepper

2 tspn tomato puree

Tomato sauce

200g (7oz) cherry tomatoes

2 tspn olive oil

2 pinches sugar

Sea salt & pepper

Fish

4 sea bream fillets
100-150g (4-5oz) each, with skin

Juice of ½ lemon

Sea salt & pepper

1 tspn olive oil

Method

For the ratatouille: Peel and dice the onions. Peel and crush the garlic. Wash and dice the tomatoes. Wash the zucchinis and aubergine, cut off the ends and dice. Wash, trim, halve and de-seed the capsicum, removing the white inner ribs, and dice. Wash the thyme, shake dry and pick off and chop the leaves. Heat the oil in a pan, add all the vegetables except the tomatoes and "sweat" for 3-4 minutes. Season with salt and pepper then add the tomato puree and tomatoes. Simmer over medium heat for 15-20 minutes, stirring occasionally.

For the tomato sauce: Whisk the cherry tomatoes to a puree in a blender with the oil and sugar. Season with salt and pepper, blend again, then strain through a sieve.

For the fish: Wash and dry the fish, score the skin with a knife, sprinkle with lemon juice and season with salt and pepper. About 5 minutes before the ratatouille is ready, heat the olive oil in a nonstick frying pan and fry the fish for 1 minute on the side without skin, then for 4-6 minutes on the skin side, until golden.

Heat the tomato sauce slowly in a small pan over a medium heat, but do not let it boil.

Season the ratatouille to taste and serve on warmed plates with the fish and the tomato sauce.

Serves 4

For a weight maintenance lunch, serve with a slice of bread.

TROUT WITH FOREST MUSHROOMS, CREAM SAUCE AND PARSLEY

2 fresh whole brook trout
(about 400g/14oz) each), cleaned

Juice of a lemon

Salt & freshly ground pepper

Butter, for greasing the dish

Mushroom sauce

600g (1.5lb) mixed mushrooms

50g (2oz) butter

3 cloves garlic, peeled and chopped

250ml (9fl oz) dry white wine

Juice of a lemon

60g (2oz) creme-fraiche (or sour cream)

Salt & freshly ground pepper

Parsley, for garnish

Method

Preheat oven to 180C (350F).

Wash the fish and dab dry. Sprinkle inside and out with lemon juice, season with salt and pepper and place in a greased dish.

For the mushroom sauce: Clean the mushrooms and cut into small pieces. Heat the butter in a large frying pan and cook (or "sweat") the garlic over very low heat for a couple of minutes. Add most of the mushrooms (leave some dry to stuff the fish with) and fry over high heat for about 5 minutes, until the liquid has evaporated. Add the white wine, stir in the lemon juice with the creme-fraiche and season with salt and pepper.

Stuff the fish with the remaining dry mushrooms, pour the sauce over and place in preheated oven for about 20 minutes, basting with the sauce from time to time. Serve garnished with parsley.

Serves 3-4

MOULES MARINIERE (MUSSELS IN WHITE WINE)

4-6 large shallots, finely chopped

5-6 garlic cloves, crushed

1 glass white wine

150ml (5fl oz) fish stock

Salt & black pepper

2kg (4lb) fresh mussels

2 tbsp chopped parsley

Method

Put the shallots, garlic, white wine and fish stock into a large saucepan and bring to the boil. Season with salt and pepper. Add mussels. Cover with a lid and cook on high heat, stirring occasionally, until all of the mussels have opened (discard any mussels that haven't opened). Sprinkle with parsley and serve.

Serves 4-5

Increasingly in Australia you can purchase mussels in vacuum packed bags. They have already been cleaned and de-bearded and are ready for the pot.

For a weight maintenance lunch serve with a small portion of risotto.

SEA BREAM WITH HERBS, BLACK OLIVES AND GARLIC

1 sea bream
(ready to cook, about 500g/1lb)

Juice of a lemon

2 tspn Herbes de Provence

2 cloves garlic

2 tbsp olive oil

Salt & pepper

100g (4oz) black olives

Method

Preheat oven to 200C (400F).

Rinse the fish inside and out with cold water and dab dry. Drizzle with lemon juice, season with salt and pepper and sprinkle with herbs. Peel and roughly chop the garlic. Put half the oil into an ovenproof dish and lay in the fish. Drizzle with the rest of the oil, add the olives and garlic and cook in the oven for 20 minutes.

Serves 2-3

Chef's tip

You can eat this dish hot or cold. At the restaurant we serve it warm: Take about six pieces of the prepared octopus plus some of the juice and olives, warm a little and toss through the rocket at the last minute.

For a weight maintenance lunch, serve with a small warm baguette.

BRAISED OCTOPUS SALAD WITH ROCKET AND GREMOLATA

⅓ cup olive oil

600g (1.5lb) baby octopus, cleaned and cut into 3 pieces each (frozen is OK if you can't find fresh)

1 small onion, finely chopped

2 cloves garlic, finely chopped

1 small red chilli, finely chopped

1 cup red wine

2 tomatoes, chopped

50g (2oz) black olives, seeded

1 bunch rocket

Gremolata

1 tspn chopped parsley

Zest of 1 orange

Zest of 1 lemon

½ clove garlic, finely chopped

Method

Heat olive oil on high heat in a deep pot until it just starts to smoke. Add the octopus (the oil will spit a little, so be careful). After 2 minutes, add the onion, garlic and chilli and cook with a lid on for 8 minutes. Add red wine, tomato and olives and cook with the lid off for a further 6 minutes. The liquid in the pan should reduce and thicken and the octopus should be tender (if not, add some water and cook a little longer).

For the gremolata: Combine parsley with the orange and lemon zests and garlic. Add to the octopus mixture, throw in some rocket and toss together before serving.

Serves 4-6

FILETS DE MAQUEREAUX A LA MOUTARDE ET AUX POIREAUX
(MACKEREL FILLET WITH DIJON MUSTARD AND LEEKS)

Olive oil

1 large leek

4 mackerel fillets (100-150g/4-5oz) each, cleaned, filleted and boned

1½ tbsp Dijon mustard

Sea salt & freshly ground pepper

1 level tbsp coriander seeds, coarsely crushed

¾ bunch of fresh oregano, chopped

Method

Preheat oven to 180C (350F).

Grease a baking tray with olive oil. Wash and clean the leek thoroughly and cut into rings. Score the skin of the mackerel with a sharp knife, then turn it over and brush the flesh with mustard. Cut each fillet in half and lightly season with salt and freshly ground pepper.

Place 4 halves of the mackerel skin-side down on the greased baking tray, cover with the leek rings, sprinkle with the crushed coriander seeds and lightly season with salt and pepper again. Top with the remaining fillets, drizzle with olive oil and bake in preheated oven for 12-15 minutes, until golden brown. Serve immediately.

Serves 4

SEARED SCALLOPS WITH LEEK AND PEA SALAD

2 leeks

1 shallot, finely sliced

100g (4oz) peas, cooked

½ bunch chives, chopped

½ bunch tarragon, picked
and chopped

50ml (2fl oz) French dressing
(see page 55)

Olive oil

20 medium scallops,
roe removed

Method

Trim the leeks down so that there is only a little amount of green left. Slice lengthways to the centre, but not all of the way in half. Rinse under cold water until all the dirt is removed. Place in a large pot of boiling, salted water and cook until tender, about 6 minutes. Remove from pot and plunge into plenty of iced water. Once cooled, drain thoroughly (overnight if possible).

Place the shallot, peas and herbs in a small bowl. Add the French dressing and set aside.

Slice the cooked leeks into rounds about ½ cm thick and place on a plate. Heat a little oil in a very hot frypan and cook the scallops. It is a good idea to do this in a couple of pans to make sure you get a good colour on the scallops. Stack each scallop on top of a leek round and spoon over the salad.

Serves 4

For a weight maintenance lunch, server with a small, warm baguette.

BOUILLABAISSE

200g (7oz) mussels

1 onion

½ leek

1 bay leaf

500ml (18fl oz) fish stock

1 large tomato

1 tbsp olive oil

100g (4oz) small squid (prepared)

400g (14oz) fish fillets
(e.g. sea bass, monkfish, whiting)

150g (5oz) shrimps, peeled
and heads removed

1 tbsp dill, chopped

1 pinch saffron threads

1 clove garlic, chopped finely

Dill sprigs, for garnish

Method

Scrub the mussels under running water, de-beard and discard any that are already open. Peel and chop the onion. Wash the leek, cut off the ends and cut into rings. Put the mussels into a pan, cover with water, add salt to taste, then the onion, leek and bay leaf and cook for 10 minutes with the lid on, shaking from time to time. When the mussels have opened, take out of the pan, strain the liquid and add to the fish stock.

Drop the tomato into boiling water for a few seconds, then skin, de-seed and dice finely. Heat the oil and sweat the tomato and squid over very low heat for 5 minutes.

Wash the fish, dab dry and cut into bite-sized pieces. Add to the stock along with the shrimps. Next add the dill, saffron and garlic and the squid, tomato and mussels and cook over low heat for 5 minutes.

Ladle into plates or bowls and serve garnished with dill.

Serves 5-7

> "
> I am healthier,
> more positive,
> have more
> energy and
> empowered
> knowing I can
> do this!
>
> *Meg Whibley*
> "

Roast duck with bacon,
oranges and broccoli
Page 105

POULTRY/RABBIT

For a weight maintenance lunch, serve with rosemary potatoes, white bread or risotto.

MEDITERRANEAN-STYLE RABBIT

1 rabbit (about 500g/1lb of meat), cleaned and boned

4-6 tbsp olive oil

2 onions

4 cloves garlic

½ tspn sea salt

200ml (7fl oz) dry white wine

½ bunch fresh rosemary

1-2 sprigs fresh thyme

50g (2oz) each of black and green olives

2 tspn dried, chopped thyme leaves

Freshly ground pepper

Juice of ½ lemon

Method

Cut the rabbit into 4 equal pieces, wash and pat dry. Remove any fat and sinew from the meat. Heat the olive oil in a roasting tin, quickly brown the rabbit pieces then set aside.

Peel the onions and cut into wedges. Peel and chop the garlic then mix it with a little sea salt and crush with a knife. Return meat to the pan with the onions and fry briefly. Stir in the white wine then add 2-3 sprigs of rosemary and thyme. Cover and simmer over a low heat for about an hour, gradually adding the stock and basting the meat frequently.

About 10 minutes before the end of cooking time, add the olives and the rest of the herbs. If necessary, top up the pan with 2-3 tbsp water. Season to taste with salt and pepper and, just before serving, squeeze the lemon juice over.

Serves 4-5

Chef's tip

Always try to use a free range
chicken breast in this dish
as the texture and flavour is
much better.

For a weight
maintenance lunch,
serve with a small
slice of bread.

ROAST CHICKEN BREAST WITH BRAISED FENNEL

2 medium fennel bulbs

3tbsp olive oil

1 clove garlic, finely chopped

5 sprigs thyme

3 tbsp white wine

100ml (4fl oz) chicken stock

4 small chicken breasts

Method

Trim and cut the fennel bulbs into 8 pieces and brown in a frying pan with the olive oil. Add the garlic and thyme, white wine and chicken stock. Cover with a lid and simmer for about 7 minutes or until the fennel is tender.

Roast the chicken breasts in a hot oven (or grill). Plate up and spoon over the braised fennel with a little of the liquid.

Serves 4

For a weight maintenance lunch, server with a small, warm baguette.

COQ AU VIN (CHICKEN IN WINE)

1 chicken (about 1kg/2lb)

Salt & pepper

1 tspn flour

100g (4oz) smoked bacon

12 shallots

200g (7oz) small button mushrooms

60g (2.5oz) clarified butter

½ litre robust red wine

½ litre chicken stock

1 clove garlic

½ bunch parsley

1 sprig thyme

1 bay leaf

50g (2oz) butter, ice cold

Method

Wash the chicken, pat dry and break into 8 pieces (legs, breast, etc). Season with salt and pepper and dust with flour. Finely dice the bacon, peel the shallots and clean the mushrooms. Heat clarified butter in a roasting dish and fry the bacon until translucent. Add the shallots and mushrooms and fry the lot together for a few minutes. Take out of the roasting dish and set aside. In the same roasting dish, first put the chicken legs in the hot fat, followed by the breast pieces, and brown all over. Add the red wine and chicken stock and bring to the boil. Return the mushrooms, bacon and shallots to the chicken.

Tie the garlic, parsley, thyme and bay leaf together to make a *bouquet garni* and put in the roasting dish. Cover and braise at a low heat for about 1 hour.

When cooked, remove the chicken pieces, mushrooms, bacon, shallots and herbs from the roasting dish and strain the liquid from the pan through a fine sieve to make a sauce. Cut the ice-cold butter into small flakes and whisk into the sauce in a pan over low heat. Do not allow to boil.

To serve, place chicken pieces, mushrooms, bacon and shallots on a large platter and pour the sauce over.

Serves 4-6

For weight loss meals or a weight maintenance dinner, exclude oranges and potatoes.

ROAST DUCK WITH BACON, ORANGES AND BROCCOLI

Weight maintenance lunch

1 medium-sized female duck
(without giblets)

Salt & pepper

3 medium-sized potatoes

1 small onion

1kg (2lb) broccoli

3 pears

2 cups flaked almonds

Olive oil

3 rashers bacon

4 oranges

100ml (4fl oz) medium-sweet white wine

1 small piece fresh ginger,
peeled and finely grated

Pepper

Method

This recipe requires preparation the night before.

Wash the duck well. Remove the neck and tail, pat dry and salt the skin liberally. Leave in the refrigerator overnight.

Preheat oven to 160C (325F)

For the stuffing: Peel the potatoes and cook in salted, boiling water until soft. Peel and finely dice the onion, blanch a third of the broccoli and then puree the lot together. Season with salt and pepper. Peel and core the pears, slice lengthwise. Dice one of the pears and mix into the puree with 1 tbsp of flaked almonds.

Stuff the duck, place in a greased roasting dish and roast in preheated oven for about 2 hours. About 20 minutes before the cooking time ends, remove and dress with the bacon strips, return to oven, raise the heat and roast until crisp and well browned.

Peel the oranges with a sharp knife and cut into slices. Heat a little oil and "sweat" the oranges over very low heat with the remaining broccoli and pear slices. Add the white wine and ginger and continue cooking gently.

Toast the remaining flaked almonds in a dry frying pan. Season the broccoli and pear to taste with salt and pepper, mix in some of the toasted almonds and arrange on a platter. Place the duck on top, brush with the roasting juices and sprinkle with leftover almonds. Serve any excess stuffing separately in a small bowl.

Serves 4-6

> " I now experiment cooking with herbs and spices that I never had the confidence to try before.
>
> *Rob Campbell*
>
> "

Provencal lamb ragout
Page 129

MEAT

This recipe is a weight maintenance lunch. For a weight loss meal exclude the pear.

SALAD OF PEAR, WALNUT AND CURLY ENDIVE WITH BAYONNE HAM

Weight maintenance lunch

1 large head frizzy endive, washed and outside leaves removed

1 pear, sliced

1tbsp walnuts, roughly chopped

75ml (2.5fl oz) French dressing (see page 55)

100g (4oz) Bayonne ham (this is the French version of prosciutto, which is also fine)

Salt & pepper

Method

Place the frizzy endive, sliced pear and walnuts into a large bowl and add the dressing. Tear the ham into the bowl (try not to let it clump), season with salt and pepper then toss the salad through your hands until well mixed. Divide between 4 bowls.

Serves 1-2

Walnuts are very popular in French cooking. The French word for walnut is noisette, which is also the name for nut.

"

I can cook
the same
meals for
my family,
participate
socially
and not
feel guilty.

Jenny Lee

"

HAM HOCK AND VEGETABLE SOUP WITH CHERVIL

3 tspn olive oil

1 shallot, peeled, halved and sliced

1 carrot, peeled and diced
(about 1cm/½ inch)

1 stick celery, trimmed and
cut into 5mm (1/4 inch) slices

1 litre (35fl oz) ham hock stock

Salt & pepper

100g (4oz) ham hock, shredded

2 tomatoes, cored and diced

25g (10oz) chervil, picked and
finely chopped

Method

Gently heat oil in a large pot. Add shallot, carrot and celery
and "sweat" over low heat for about 2 minutes, until softened.
Add the stock and season with salt and pepper. Bring to the
boil and skim off any impurities. Reduce heat, cover with
the lid slightly askew and simmer for 15 minutes. Add the
shredded ham hock, tomatoes and chervil and simmer for
another 1-2 minutes. Serve.

Serves 1-2

Be careful when you season this dish as the ham hock can
be salty. You can vary this recipe using chicken stock and
shredded chicken instead of the ham hock.

Perfect for a weight loss or weight maintenance breakfast or a weight maintenance lunch.

SEMI-DRIED TOMATOES AND HAM ON TOAST WITH RICOTTA

4 large roma tomatoes, cored and cut in half

4 tspn olive oil

Salt & pepper

¼ bunch fresh thyme

4 slices ham

50g (2oz) fresh ricotta

4 slices multigrain toast

Method

Lay the halved tomatoes out on a tray and sprinkle with the olive oil, salt and pepper and thyme sprigs. Dry in oven at 120C (2560F) for 3-4 hours.

Place the toast on the plates, lay a slice of ham, add the semi-dried tomatoes and sprinkle with fresh ricotta.

Serves 4

The tomatoes can be dried days in advance and will keep well in the fridge. To take away the chill, before serving reheat in the oven on medium heat for about 3 minutes (or in a microwave for about 15 seconds).

Chef's tip

In France, calves liver is about the same price as a good steak. In Australia it is considerably cheaper. Try to look for liver that is as fresh as possible; it should be a nice bright pink and not smell. Trim as much of the veins out as you can.

For a weight maintenance lunch, serve with a slice of bread.

GRILLED CALVES LIVER WITH CRISP MUSHROOMS AND SEEDED MUSTARD SAUCE

40ml (1fl oz) vegetable oil

300g (10oz) mixed mushrooms (not field mushrooms, as they are too thick)

1 shallot, finely diced

½ bunch parsley, chopped

Salt & pepper

100ml (4fl oz) veal jus

1 tspn seeded mustard

20ml (1/2fl oz) French dressing (see page 55)

12 slices of liver, about 1cm (½ inch) thick

Method

In a hot fry pan, heat the vegetable oil, add the mixed mushrooms and fry until they start to turn golden brown and crispy, about 8 minutes (all of the liquid should have evaporated). When the mushrooms are crispy, add the shallot and parsley, season with salt and pepper and drain off any excess oil.

In a small saucepan, mix the veal jus, seeded mustard and French dressing and bring to the boil to make a sauce.

Brush the liver with vegetable oil, season with salt and pepper and grill on a hot plate or BBQ for about 45 seconds each side. Cook for longer if you don't like blood. Place on a plate, cover with the mushrooms and drizzle the mustard sauce over.

Serves 4-6

You can buy veal jus in supermarkets; it is basically veal stock reduced until it is thickened slightly and the flavour has intensified.

For a weight maintenance lunch, serve with a small, warm baguette.

FILLET STEAK WITH TARRAGON AND GREEN ASPARAGUS

800g (2lb) green asparagus

25g (1oz) butter

Olive oil

4 shallots, finely diced

100ml (4fl oz) white wine

25ml (11/2 tbsp) thick double cream

1 tbsp wholegrain mustard

1 clove garlic, finely chopped

6 tbsp freshly chopped tarragon

Sea salt & freshly ground pepper

6 fillet steaks (150g/5oz each)

Method

Wash the asparagus and cut off the woody ends. Blanch in plenty of boiling, salted water for 10 minutes then drain. Melt the butter in a frying pan and gently toss the asparagus in the butter. Keep warm.

Heat 2 tbsp olive oil in a frying pan and gently fry the shallots until translucent. Add the wine and cook over a medium heat for 3 minutes. Reduce the heat then add the double cream, mustard, garlic, tarragon, salt and pepper. Allow to slowly infuse over a low heat.

Meanwhile, heat a little olive oil in a large frying pan and fry the steaks over high heat for 1½-3 minutes each side, depending on how well done you like it.

To serve, rest steak on top of the asparagus and spoon the sauce over.

Serves 6 (adjust steak size to your allowance)

SOURIS D'AGNEAU
(LAMB SHANK ON TOMATOES AND CAPSICUM)

4 small lamb shanks

2 stalks each of parsley, marjoram, rosemary and thyme

6 tbsp olive oil

Salt & freshly ground pepper

4 cloves garlic

2 strips each of orange and lemon peel

800g (2lb) vine tomatoes

1 red and 1 yellow capsicum (large)

250ml (9fl oz) meat stock

125ml (4.5fl oz) dry white wine

Method

Preheat oven to 180C (350F)

Wipe down the lamb shanks. Carefully wash the herbs, shake dry and chop finely. Mix the herbs with 4 tbsp olive oil, salt and pepper and spread on the lamb shanks. Leave to stand for about 2 hours.

Peel and halve the garlic cloves. Brush a baking tray with the rest of the olive oil. Put the lamb shanks, garlic, orange and lemon peel in the baking tray and roast in preheated oven for about 1½ hours, basting frequently with the meat juices.

Wash the tomatoes. Trim, wash and quarter the capsicum. About 30 minutes before the cooking time ends, put the vegetables in the baking tray with the meat and add the stock and white wine.

When done, transfer the lamb shanks and vegetables to a large serving dish and pour over the strained roasting juices.

Serves 4

For a weight maintenance lunch, serve with a warm slice of bread.

AGNEAU BRAISE AVEC DES HARICOTS BLANCS
(BRAISED LAMB WITH WHITE BEANS)

1 large onion

4 cloves garlic

3 tomatoes

150g (5oz) smoked, cured belly pork
(sliced 5mm/½ inch thick)

4 tbsp olive oil

4 slices lamb from the shoulder,
about 100g (4oz) each

2 tspn paprika

3 tbsp lemon juice

150ml (5fl oz) white wine

400ml (14fl oz) vegetable stock

100g (4oz) large white beans
(e.g. butter beans), soaked
overnight then drained

Salt & pepper

Basil, shredded

Method

You will need to soak the beans overnight.

Peel and finely chop the onion and garlic. Wash the tomatoes and cut into wedges. Cut the belly pork into pieces.

Heat oil in a large pan over high heat and quickly brown the lamb on all sides. Take out of the pan and set aside. Add the onion to the pan with the belly pork and fry in the same oil for 4-5 minutes. Return the lamb to the pan with the garlic, paprika and 2 tbsp lemon juice. Add the wine and stock, cover with a lid and braise over a low heat for 1½-2 hours. About 40 minutes before the end of cooking time, add the drained white beans and the tomatoes. Add a little water to the pan if necessary.

To serve, sprinkle over the remaining lemon juice and season to taste with salt and pepper. Serve in deep plates garnished with shredded basil.

Serves 4-6

> " It is easy to commit to Bodytrim as the food is so natural and nourishing, plenty of vegetables and regular protein with my meals and snacks.

Rob Stoutley

"

LAMB FILLET, BEETROOT AND MINT SALAD

1 bunch medium beetroots

1 bunch mint, picked

2 shallots, thinly sliced

50ml (1.5fl oz) walnut oil

1 tbsp sherry vinegar

Salt & pepper

8 lamb fillets (about 50g/2oz each)

Method

Requires about 2 hours to cook beetroot.

Take all but 1 of the beetroots and wrap in foil. Bake in a low oven for about 2 hours until soft (like a jacket potato). Cool a little, remove the skin and slice thinly. Cut the remaining beetroot into matchsticks and mix this with the mint and shallots, add the walnut oil and sherry vinegar and toss. Season the lamb fillets and sear in a hot pan or BBQ (they should be quite pink inside).

To serve, lay the cooked beetroot slices on plates. Slice the lamb, mix in with the salad then place on top of the beetroot slices.

Serves 3-4

> "
> I am convinced that this system is the most natural and effective method of becoming a healthier and trimmer person!
>
> *Teresa Sokkar*
> "

BOEUF AU BORDEAUX (BEEF IN RED WINE)

Weight maintenance lunch

Marinade

1 large bunch mixed soup vegetables
(e.g. carrot, leek, celeriac, parsley)

3 cloves garlic

1 tspn black peppercorns

650ml (25fl oz) dry red wine
(e.g. Burgundy, Bordeaux)

1kg beef (from the shoulder)

Salt & pepper

2-3 tbsp flour

4 tbsp olive oil, for frying

1-2 tbsp tomato puree

100g (4oz) bacon, diced

1 bunch shallots, peeled and
cut into strips

80ml (3fl oz) sherry

3 cups veal stock

1 'floury' potato (about 150g/5oz)

200g (7oz) mushrooms

120g (4oz) olives, mixed

1 tbsp pickled green peppercorns

Rosemary, for garnish

Method

This recipe requires preparation the night before.

Make the marinade the day before: Clean and finely dice the soup vegetables, peel and chop the garlic then combine with the black peppercorns and red wine. Tie the meat into shape with kitchen string and place in the marinade, making sure it is completely covered by the liquid (add more wine if necessary). Cover and put in a cool place overnight.

Preheat oven to 175C (330F).

Take the meat out of the marinade, pat dry, season with salt and pepper and dust with flour. Keep the marinade. Heat the oil in a roasting dish on the stovetop and brown the meat on all sides. Add the tomato puree and diced bacon, followed by the shallots, and cook briefly. Add the sherry and simmer to reduce slightly. Strain a little of the marinade into the roasting dish and simmer again until reduced. Then add the rest of the marinade and the stock and bring to the boil. Peel the potato and grate finely into the stock. Put the roasting dish into preheated oven for about 2½ hours.

While the meat is cooking, clean the mushrooms, halving any large ones. When done, take the meat out of the stock, wrap in aluminium foil and leave to rest.

To make the sauce, remove half the vegetables from the stock, puree in a blender and reheat in a pan. Add the mushrooms and simmer for 10 minutes. Return to stock.

To serve, slice meat, pour over the sauce, scatter with olives and green peppercorns and garnish with rosemary.

Serves 6-10

Chef's tip

Ratatouille should be cooked quickly, as it loses its appeal when stewed for a long time.

VEAL ESCALOPE WITH RATATOUILLE

600g (1.5lb) veal escalope

Ratatouille

2 tbsp olive oil

½ medium eggplant, diced

½ onion, finely chopped

1 clove garlic, finely chopped

1 red capsicum, diced

1 zucchini, diced

4 tomatoes, diced

¼ tspn chopped basil

Salt & pepper

Method

Heat a large frypan with the olive oil on a high heat and cook the eggplant for 1 minute. Add the onion, garlic and capsicum and cook a further 2 minutes. Add the zucchini and cook another minute. Add the diced tomato and basil and cook until the tomato starts to break down. Season with salt and pepper to taste.

Gently fry the veal escalops for 30 seconds each side and serve on top of a bed of ratatouille

Serves 4-6

PROVENCAL LAMB RAGOUT

400g (1lb) lamb, from the leg

2 onions

3 cloves garlic

1 aubergine (eggplant)

2 courgettes

1 red, 1 green and 1 yellow capsicum

5 tbsp olive oil

400ml (14fl oz) red wine

300g (11oz) chopped tomatoes (tinned)

4 sprigs thyme

1 sprig rosemary

Salt & freshly ground pepper

Method

Wash the meat, pat dry and cube. Peel and chop the onions and garlic. Wash and trim the aubergine, quarter lengthwise and slice. Wash, trim and slice the courgettes. Wash and halve the capsicum, remove the seeds and white inner ribs and roughly dice.

Heat 3 tbsp oil in a pan and brown the meat on all sides. Add the onion and garlic and fry briefly, then stir in the red wine. Add the tomatoes and herbs, cover and cook over a low heat for about 1½ hours.

Heat the rest of the oil and briefly cook the aubergine and courgettes over low heat. Add the capsicum and fry for about 2 minutes, until cooked but still retaining a little bite. Mix the vegetables with the meat, cook for about 2 minutes and season to taste with salt and pepper. Serve with a baguette.

Serves 4

POACHED FILLET OF BEEF WITH SPINACH
AND GREEN PEPPERCORNS

4 x 100-150g (4-5oz) fillet steaks

200g (7oz) spinach

1 tbsp olive oil

2 tspn green peppercorns

A splash of brandy (optional)

Poaching stock

3 litres veal stock

6 large field mushrooms, sliced

2 bay leaves

2 sprigs thyme

Method

Place all the poaching stock ingredients into a fairly deep pot, bring to the boil and simmer for 20 minutes. Tie a piece of string around each fillet steak and then the other end to a wooden spoon. Rest the wooden spoon across the top of the pot so that the steak hangs immersed in the poaching liquid, but not touching the bottom. Cook in the simmering stock for 5-6 minutes then allow to rest for a further 5 minutes in a warm place.

Saute the spinach in a little olive oil, place on a platter and keep warm.

Take about 200ml (7fl oz) of the poaching stock and boil until the liquid has reduced by half. Add green peppercorns, and a splash of brandy if you like. Untie the beef fillet and place on top of the spinach. Spoon the peppercorn sauce over.

Serves 4

The French name for this dish is Fillet Ficelle or "fillet on a string". Poaching is a very gentle way of cooking the meat so it is always very tender.

BEEF BOURGUIGNON

750g (2lb) lean beef

300g (10oz) carrots

200g (7oz) celery

300g (10oz) brown button mushrooms

400g (14oz) shallots or small onions

6 tbsp olive oil

2 cloves garlic

½ litre (18fl oz) robust red wine

2 bay leaves

1 litre beef broth or vegetable stock

3-4 sprigs rosemary

50g (2oz) diced ham or bacon

Salt & freshly ground black pepper

Method

Dice the meat (not too small). Clean and wash the carrots and celery and cut into bite-sized pieces. Clean the mushrooms and set aside. Peel the onions and cut in half. Heat 4 tbsp oil in a pan and saute the meat, in batches if necessary. Add the onions and garlic and cook on very low heat until they begin to soften. Add the red wine and cook until reduced by half. Add the bay leaves and stock and cook over a low heat for a further 1½ hours. About 20 minutes before the end of cooking time, add the carrots and celery.

Meanwhile, strip the leaves from the rosemary stalks and chop finely. Fry the bacon in the remaining oil, add the mushrooms and stew for 5 minutes. Season with salt and pepper, mix into the beef and sprinkle with rosemary before serving.

Serves 6-8

Chef's tip

Lamb neck is one of my favourite cuts of lamb. It has an amazing flavour and texture. This dish can be prepared in advance and warmed up on the day.

For a weight maintenance lunch, serve with a small baked potato.

BRAISED LAMB NECK WITH SAUCE BASQUAISE

600g (1.5lb) boned lamb neck,
cut into 4 pieces

Salt & pepper

1 carrot, chopped

1 stick of celery, chopped

1 onion, chopped

1 bay leaf

2 sprigs thyme

1 litre lamb (or chicken) stock

2 red capsicums

1.5 large tins tomatoes, crushed

50g (2oz) black olives

Zest of 1 orange

Method

Allow 3 hours for preparation and cooking time.

Season lamb neck with salt and pepper and brown on all sides in a frying pan. Remove meat from the pan, put in the chopped carrot, celery, onion, bay leaf and thyme and brown also. Place the lamb and the vegetables together in a casserole dish and cover with the stock. Cook in the oven on low heat for about 2 hours.

Cut the capsicums into 4 lengthways, remove the stalk and seeds and grill skin-side up for about 10 minutes or until the skin is blistering and blackening. Put into a bowl, cover with clingfilm and leave for about 10 minutes. Remove the skin and cut into strips. Place the tomatoes in a pot and cook down by about half then add the capsicum, olives and orange zest. Cook a further 20 minutes (the sauce should be quite thick).

To serve, place the sauce in 4 bowls, put lamb neck on top and spoon over some of the braising liquid.

Serves 4-6

"

I love the
free day and
the fact that
I can still
lose weight.

Maria Cotts

"

Recipes

4 YOUR FREE DAY

QUICHE LORRAINE

1 tart tin (30cm/12inch diameter)
or 6-8 tartlet tins

Pastry

1⅔ cups flour

125g (4oz) cold butter

A pinch of salt

1 egg

Filling

50g (2oz) cooked ham,
in slices ½cm (1/4 inch) thick

100g (4oz) mild, raw ham,
 sliced thinly

3-4 onions

1 bunch mixed fresh herbs
(whatever is in season)

3 cloves garlic

4 eggs

200g (7oz) freshly grated gruyere
(or any hard cheese)

200g (7oz) cream

Salt and freshly ground black pepper

Method

Preheat oven to 200C (400F).

Put the flour in a heap on the work surface, mix in the salt and make a well in the middle. Cut the cold butter into small pieces and scatter around the well. Break the egg into the middle and chop all the ingredients with a knife until they have the consistency of breadcrumbs, then quickly knead to a dough using your hands. Form into a ball, wrap in foil or clingfilm and chill for about 30 minutes.

For the filling: Dice both sorts of ham. Peel and finely chop the onions. Wash and dry the herbs and chop very finely. Mix everything together in a bowl. Peel the garlic and crush into the bowl.

In another bowl, whisk the eggs and stir in the cheese and cream. Season with salt and pepper.

Roll out the chilled pastry on a work surface dusted with flour and line the tart tin (or tartlet tins). Put into preheated oven (middle shelf) and prebake for about 10 minutes (if using small tartlet tins, prebake for about 8 minutes). Remove from oven.

Spread the filling onto the pastry, pour the cheese and cream mixture over and bake a further 40-45 minute or until done. Serve lukewarm.

Serves 3-4

ONION SOUP WITH TOASTED BREAD AND CHEESE

1kg (2lb) onions

50g (2oz) butter

1 litre (35fl oz) vegetable stock

250ml (9fl oz) dry white wine

A pinch of nutmeg

1 tspn fresh (or ½ tspn dried) thyme

A pinch of ground caraway seeds

1 bunch parsley

4 slices baguette

2 cloves garlic, peeled

Salt & freshly ground pepper

50g (2oz) raclette cheese, grated

Method

Peel the onions and cut into thin strips. Heat the butter in a pan and cook the onions on very low heat until translucent. Add the stock and the wine, then the nutmeg, thyme and caraway seeds and simmer for 25-30 minutes.

Toast the baguette slices and rub with the peeled garlic, then crush the garlic and stir into the soup, season to taste with salt and pepper and ladle into heat-proof bowls.

To serve, float the baguette slices on top of the soup, sprinkle with cheese and put under the grill for about 5 minutes, until the cheese has melted. Serve immediately.

Serves 4

To use this recipe for weight loss exclude the apples and the potato.

POULET VALLEE D'AUGE
(CHICKEN WITH CIDER AND APPLES)

1 chicken (about 1kg/2lb)

Salt & freshly ground pepper

200g (7oz) onions

1 apple

1 tbsp butter

1 tbsp olive oil

1 clove garlic

250ml (9fl oz) cider

250ml (9fl oz) chicken stock

1 bay leaf

1 sprig thyme

2 sage leaves

1 sprig rosemary

100g (4oz) creme fraiche (or sour cream)

800g (2lb) potatoes

1 tbsp snipped chives

1 apple

1 tbsp lemon juice

Method

Preheat oven to 180C (350F).

Wash the chicken, pat dry and joint into 8 pieces. Season with salt and pepper. Peel and chop the onions. Peel, quarter and core the apple and cut into small pieces.

Heat the butter and olive oil in a roasting dish and brown the chicken pieces on all sides. Take the chicken breasts out of the roasting dish and set aside.

Add the onions and apple to the roasting dish. Peel the garlic, crush into the dish and cook briefly over very low heat. Add the cider, chicken stock and herbs, cover with a lid and cook in preheated oven (middle shelf) for about 15 minutes. Return the chicken breasts to the roasting dish and cook, without a lid, for a further 15 minutes or so. Remove chicken from the dish and keep warm.

Strain the sauce from the roasting dish through a sieve into a pan, stir in the creme fraiche and bring to the boil. Simmer until reduced slightly and season with salt and pepper.

Meanwhile, peel the potatoes and boil for about 25 minutes. Wash, quarter and core the second apple, cut into thin sticks and mix with the lemon juice.

To serve, put the chicken pieces on plates with the sauce and scatter with apple sticks and snipped chives. Serve with the boiled potatoes.

Serves 4-5

> I have learnt about portion sizes as well as food in moderation.
>
> *Matt Davidson*

TRUFFADE
(POTATO WITH CHEESE AND BACON)

500g (1lb) potatoes

1 shallot

4 eggs

100ml (4fl oz) cream

100g (4oz) banon cheese

Salt & freshly ground black pepper

2 tbsp purified butter or lard

200g (7oz) jambon sec d'Auvergne (bacon), thinly sliced

100g (4oz) laguiole cheese, grated

Frisee lettuce, for garnish

Method

Clean the potatoes and boil in plenty of salted water for 30 minutes until soft. Peel and finely chop the shallot. Drain the potatoes, allow to cool, then peel and cut into thin slices.

Separate the eggs. Beat the egg yolks, then add the cream and banon cheese and season with salt and pepper. Add the shallots. Whip the egg whites stiffly and fold into the egg-cream mixture.

Butter a non-stick frying pan with half of the purified butter and layer with half the bacon and half of the laguiole cheese. Cover with 4 tbsp of the egg mixture and a layer of potato slices. Season with salt and pepper. Pour the rest of the egg mixture over the potatoes and spread evenly by shaking the frying pan. Sprinkle the remaining cheese and bacon over the top. Slowly heat the frying pan and cover with a lid.

Cook for 10–15 minutes over low to moderate heat, until set. Turn over by using a lid or plate and cook on the other side for a further 5 minutes. Cut into quarters and serve with the frisee leaves.

Serves 4

Banon is an unpasteurised, hard cheese made from cow's milk.

Laguiole is a creamy, unpasteurised, natural-rind cheese made from a mixture of cow's, sheep's and goat's milk.

CHERRY CLAFOUTIS WITH ICING SUGAR

500g (1lb) sour cherries (from a jar or use stoned, fresh cherries)

1 tbsp melted butter, for greasing the dishes

3 eggs

2 tbsp icing sugar

40g (1⅓oz) flour

200ml (7fl oz) milk

Icing sugar, for sprinkling

Method

Preheat the oven to 180C (350F).

Drain the cherries. Brush 1 large or 4 small baking dishes lightly with melted butter. Beat the eggs and the icing sugar until very frothy. Sieve the flour over the beaten eggs, add the milk and mix to a batter.

Pour the batter into the baking dishes and scatter with the cherries. Bake in preheated oven for about 25 minutes, until golden brown. Take the clafoutis out of the oven and leave to cool slightly. Serve sprinkled with icing sugar.

Serves 4

CREME CARAMEL

90g (3oz) sugar

2 egg yolks

3 eggs

500ml (16 fl oz) milk

½ vanilla pod

For the caramel

100g (4oz) sugar

1 tbsp water

4 x ramekins, lightly greased

Method

Put the sugar, eggs and egg yolks into a bowl and mix well. Slit the vanilla pod open lengthwise, then put the milk into a pan with the vanilla pod and bring to the boil. Gradually stir the hot milk into the egg and sugar mixture.

For the caramel: Put the sugar into a small pan with the water and simmer until golden brown. Pour immediately into the lightly greased moulds, filling them to a depth of about 3 mm. Next, strain the custard mixture through a sieve and fill up the moulds.

Fill a large baking dish with hot water to a depth of about 2 cm. Stand the moulds in the water and put into the oven at 180C for about 30 minutes, until set. Take out and leave to cool completely.

To serve, run the tip of a sharp knife around the edges of the moulds and turn out onto plates.

Serves 4

> " " I can enjoy some sweets in my eating plan and still lose weight. How fantastic!
>
> *Hollie Jones*

SOUFFLE AU KIRSCH
(KIRSCH SOUFFLE)

300ml (10fl oz)milk

1 vanilla pod

80g (3oz)sugar

50g (2oz) butter

50g (2oz) flour

6 eggs

80ml (3fl oz) Kirsch d'Alsace
(cherry brandy)

Icing sugar, for dusting

Method

Preheat oven to 175C (330F).

Put the milk into a pan and bring to the boil. Slit open the vanilla pod, scrape out the seeds and add to the milk with the pod and the sugar. Remove from the heat and leave to stand.

In another pan, melt the butter and stir in the flour. Remove vanilla pod from the milk. Stir milk into the butter and flour. Bring to a vigorous boil, stirring constantly, then remove from the heat and leave to cool slightly. Butter the souffle dishes and sprinkle with sugar.

Separate the eggs and gradually beat the yolks and the kirsch into the white sauce. Beat the egg whites until stiff then fold lightly into the mixture.

Fill the souffle dishes ¾ full with the mixture and bake in preheated oven for about 15 minutes, until well risen and golden on top. Do not open the oven while they are cooking. When done, remove from oven, dust with icing sugar and serve immediately.

Serves 4-6

CREME BRULEE

1 vanilla pod

250ml (9fl oz) milk

250ml (9fl oz) cream

3 eggs

2 egg yolks

75g (1⅔lb) sugar

Cane sugar, for dusting

METHOD

Scrape the seeds from the vanilla pod then put the milk, cream, the seeds and the pod into a pan and bring to the boil. Beat the eggs and egg yolks with the sugar until creamy, but not frothy. Remove the vanilla pod from the hot milk then gradually stir mixture into the creamed sugar. Strain through a sieve and pour into six ramekins.

Place the ramekins in a roasting tin or baking dish and add hot water two-thirds of the way up the sides of the ramekins. Bake in the oven at 200C for about 20 minutes or until set. Cool and put into the refrigerator.

Before serving, sprinkle the cremes with brown sugar and put under a hot grill until the surface caramelises (alternatively, stand in a dish of ice-cold water and put into a very hot oven until the top forms a crust). Serve hot.

Serves 6

BODYTRIM SUCCESS STORIES

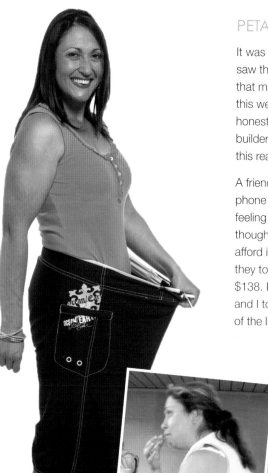

PETA ADAMS

It was like a miracle from above when I saw the Bodytrim ad on the TV. I thought that maybe there was something to this weight loss plan because, let's be honest, it was created by an ex body builder and a doctor. I thought, could this really be my salvation?

A friend encouraged me to pick up the phone in the end. But even then I was feeling half-hearted about it because I thought for sure I wouldn't be able to afford it. So I was blown away when they told me the whole kit was only $138. I ordered it then and there – and I told myself that this was the end of the line for me. If this didn't work,

then I would have to stay obese because I just couldn't face the ups and downs any more, losing the weight only to see it pile back on.

After my first week on Bodytrim I lost 2 kilos. But something even stranger happened: I wasn't starving all the time! Not only was my hunger satisfied, but I watched the weight melt away. I gave up all the strenuous exercise and concentrated on food and walking.

Every time I hit a bad patch, I would tune in to Bodytrim TV and it always seemed Geoff and Chris would be there with a solution to the very problem I was having at the time.

Suddenly, as I neared my goal weight, everywhere I went people stared at me in amazement. Some friends hardly recognised me at first. I was elated.

I never thought the day would come when I could be a normal weight for my height, but it did come and it was Bodytrim that got me there.

LEAH CHALWELL

My parents fed our large family on the basics, meat and two veg for dinner, and taught us to fill-up on cereals. I can still hear my Dad saying, 'If you are still hungry, have a bowl of Weeties.'

Dad grew up during the Depression, fought in WW II and was a prisoner of war, so our eating habits as a family derived from his reasoning that it wasn't pleasant going hungry, and that the price of freedom had been paid to do and eat what you liked. Keeping in mind that, as a regular church-goer, I was also taught that gluttony or 'pigging out' was a selfish act and not a pretty characteristic in any person. This mentality stuck with me and so I never said 'no' to any food placed before me, as it was a given gift, but at the same time I never went searching for a pig-out feast.

I can't believe the amount of money I must have wasted over the years buying diet shakes and joining gyms. Now I am so thrilled to be able to have paid a one-off fee for knowledge that will stay with me forever. And I can pass this wisdom onto my children and they in turn their own children. You cannot put a price on that.

For me, since the first 20kg came off it hasn't been so much about losing the weight fast as applying the Bodytrim system to my lifestyle - and the fact I won't ever again struggle with my weight because I now know the secret!!

I am happy to live my God-given life now, educated about food choices and without any worries or obsessions about weight. I encourage anybody to keep challenging their ideas about food and to learn properly about healthy eating. Bodytrim really is life altering.

I would suggest people start with one step at a time. First, concentrate on the type of foods you eat, then your portions sizes, and leave the exercise until you have totally understood and put into practice 70% of the 90% weight loss food equation. Doing it this way helped me to gain strong, good habits from the very beginning.

Also, don't stress the little things like having a bad day. Actually, just don't stress at all! Bodytrim is a lifestyle not a diet. All it takes is the desire and commitment to yourself that you will change your life the minute you order the kit.

INDEX